# THE
# BIG
# TEASE

# THE BIG TEASE

## Gary Wilmot

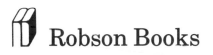 Robson Books

First published in Great Britain in 1988 by Robson Books Ltd, Bolsover House, 5–6 Clipstone Street, London W1P 7EB.

Copyright © 1988 Gary Wilmot

British Library Cataloguing in Publication Data

Wilmot, Gary
  The big tease.
  I. Title
  793.8
  ISBN 0–86051–548–6

**Printed in Great Britain by
Billing & Sons Ltd, Worcester**

# INTRODUCTION

*The Big Tease* is a collection of tricks, teasers, puzzles and illusions of all kinds, collected over the years from a wide variety of sources. Some have been told to me by friends, some by colleagues, some even came from my postbag. They include amazing feats of strength, balancing tricks, optical illusions, magic tricks, mind-reading, mathematical mind-benders, verbal teasers, word puzzles and riddles. Many will make you scratch your head in bewilderment; some will make you laugh; several will surprise you, and a few may even astound you; but all will, I hope, provide hours of entertainment for every member of the family.

What do you get if you cross a cocoa bean with an elk?

**Answer**
A chocolate moose.

How do you start a milk pudding race?

**Answer**
Sago.

Why did the pixie eat slowly?

**Answer**
Because he knew that goblin his food was bad for his 'elf.

What do you call a musical insect?

**Answer**
A humbug.

# EYE SIGHT

What better way to start than by playing a trick on a friend? He'd better be a good friend, or you might upset him. Just tell him that you would like to test his eyesight. He's not likely to object. Then ask him to point a finger to one of his temples, to read the four letters on the chart you place before him, and to name the object drawn at the bottom of the chart.

This is what the chart will look like:

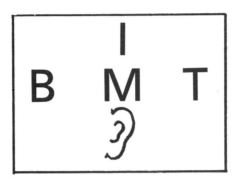

And this is what your friend will say:

'I, B, M, T, ear.'

*Now's the time to run!*

## ALL GREEK

Around 300 years B.C. the Greek philosopher Aristotle, when not busy founding the Peripatetic school of Athens, discovered the following strange phenomenon. If you cross the index finger of one hand over the middle finger next to it, and then touch a marble with the ends of those two fingers, you will find that you can feel two marbles. Strange, isn't it?

# HANDY MAN

If you think you're so clever that you'd never have fallen for the previous trick, see if you can answer this challenge. Put your left hand where your right hand cannot reach it. OK? That's all.

Have you managed it yet? What, you found it impossible? It isn't, you know.

**Answer**

Cup your left hand round your right elbow.

\*\*\*\*\*\*\*\*\*\*\*\*\*\*\*\*\*\*\*\*\*\*\*\*\*\*\*\*\*\*\*\*\*

What can a whole orange do that half an orange can't do?

Look round!

\*\*\*\*\*\*\*\*\*\*\*\*\*\*\*\*\*\*\*\*\*\*\*\*\*\*\*\*\*\*\*\*\*

# MATCH FOR A MATCH?

While on the subject of fingers, see if yours are stronger than a matchstick. Put the matchstick across your middle finger and below the index and ring fingers, at about the level of the joint nearest the nails. Now, by pressing upwards with the middle finger and downwards with the other two fingers, see if you can break the match. Sounds simple, doesn't it?

Having difficulty? Don't be surprised if you find it impossible – because it is! But try moving the match further down your fingers, nearer to the knuckles, and you should manage it. It's all a question of leverage.

# ROLLING RACE

If you want to have fun with the children in a little contest you can be sure of winning, then suggest a rolling race. You will need a flat board, propped up at one end, down which objects can be rolled. You should also have a small ball, a flat disc such as a frisbee, and a hoop of some kind, such as a tyre or a hula hoop. Each of you chooses one object – and if you want to win, make sure you choose the ball. Stand with them level at the top of the slope, and then let them roll down at a shout of 'Go!'

No matter what the size of the objects, the ball will always win, the flat disc will come second, and the hoop will come last. Even a marble would beat a hula hoop. Why, you may ask? Well, I can't answer you precisely, but it is one of those laws of physics which *always* works.

## TIPPING THE BALANCE

For this test of your skill and co-ordination you will need one, two or even three oranges.

All you have to do is to balance them on your forehead. It's very easy – just tip back your head and place an orange on it. If it stays still, place another orange on top of the first. It's easiest if you place the oranges with either the stalk or the calyx end on your forehead, because the fruit is flatter there. Keep practising – it's a good party trick, though you may feel a proper nana if someone sees you before you've got it quite right.

## BANANA SPLIT

Here's a fruity little teaser that will astonish all the family. The idea is to slice a banana – *inside its skin*. Anyone then peeling the banana – which will fall apart in his lap – will be open-mouthed with astonishment. You can even turn it into a bet. Imagine betting someone that the next banana they eat out of the fruit bowl will be ready-sliced. They'd be bound to take you on, wouldn't they? Or, if you think there's a chance that they may choose an 'ordinary' banana, you can bet them that the next one *you* take will be ready-sliced.

That is all very well, but how is it done, I hear you asking. Well, like all good tricks it is very simple. All you need is a needle, which you insert near one end of the fruit along one of its 'seams'. You then wiggle the needle from side to side, and it will slice the banana. Take the needle out, and then insert it a little further down and repeat the operation. Do it along the entire length of the fruit for a really astonishing effect. It is as well not to do it too soon before the banana is likely to be eaten, for the fruit will quickly turn brown and go bad.

# WRECKED ANGLES

The drawing below shows a rectangular lake in the centre of which is a rectangular island. On the edge of the lake stands a man determined to get to the island. But the lake is very deep, it is too far from the shore to the island to jump, and the man cannot swim. However, he has two planks, each of which is exactly as long as the lake is wide. A plank, therefore, will not make a bridge, for it is not long enough.

   How, without getting wet, can the man get to the island?

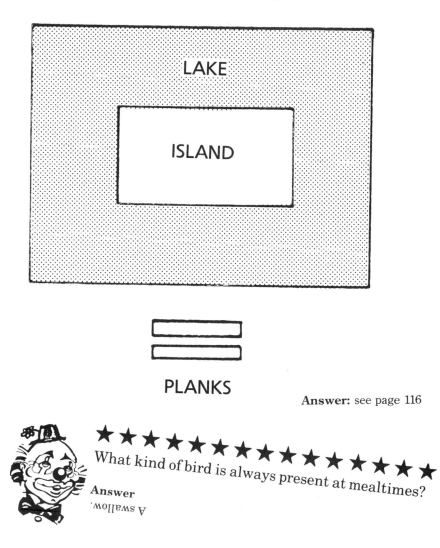

LAKE

ISLAND

PLANKS

**Answer:** see page 116

★ ★ ★ ★ ★ ★ ★ ★ ★ ★ ★ ★ ★ ★ ★ ★ ★ ★ ★ ★ ★ ★
What kind of bird is always present at mealtimes?

**Answer**
A swallow.

11

# STRAWDINARY!

Here's another teaser to try out on the children. It needs a couple of ordinary straws, and a glass of their favourite drink.

Now, you'd think that drinking through two straws would be easier than drinking through one, wouldn't you? You'd get twice as much of the drink in your mouth? Try it with one straw in the drink and the other dangling down outside the glass, and see what happens. Or get your children to try it, and see what they make of it. How quickly can they finish the drink using this method?

You, and they, will quickly discover that nothing at all happens. None of the drink travels up either straw, and while you're waiting to work out why, you could die of thirst.

The point is that the straw outside the glass acts as a kind of 'leak' to your suction system, and therefore the other straw doesn't work either. It may be frustrating, but it's a good trick to try on someone.

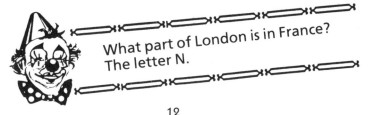

What part of London is in France? The letter N.

# VOWEL LANGUAGE

Can you think of two English words that contain the vowels a, e, i, o and u once only, and in the correct alphabetical order?

# CRACKERS

If you know someone who is rather greedy, try this challenge on them. Make a bet with them that they can't eat three cream crackers or plain water biscuits one after the other without having anything to drink. It's very difficult, if not impossible, to do.

# CHILD'S PLAY

This is a trick to try with someone who is obviously less strong than you are. Ask him to lift his elbows up to shoulder level, and then hold his hands towards each other horizontally so the tips of the forefingers just touch. Stand facing your partner, grasp his wrists, and steadily, without taking him by surprise or jerking, try and pull his fingers apart. Funnily enough, you won't be able to do it.

# PENNIES FROM HEAVEN

This trick is one I always longed to be able to do when I was young, and it is still one of my favourites. Once you have mastered it you can make coins and other small objects materialize from thin air, from behind people's ears and other extraordinary places, and you will never fail to astonish them.

There are six basic ways of 'palming'. Here they are.

**1.** Gripping the coin between the fleshy base of your thumb and the other fleshy area at the edge of your hand.

**2.** Gripping the coin between the index and middle fingers. With this grip you can hold your hand by your side and keep the coin hidden.

**3.** Gripping the coin between the thumb and index finger.

**4.** Holding the hand in a curled, natural position and gripping the coin with the upper part of the middle and ring fingers.

**5.** As above, but holding the coin with the tips of the middle and index fingers.

**6.** Holding the coin on the back of your hand, gripping it between the index and little fingers. This is difficult to master, but it does enable you to show that you have nothing in your hand – at any rate in the palm.

All these grips take a bit of practice, and you may find one easier to master than the others, because of factors like the length and suppleness of your fingers.

# ALL SQUARE

If you have managed to make twelve coins materialize from thin air, arrange them in a square like this, with four coins along each side.

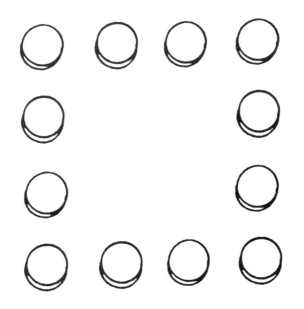

Using the same twelve coins, now form another square, with five coins along each side. It *is* possible!

**Answer:** see page 116

What's the difference between a drum and a cook?

**Answer** One makes a din, the other makes a dinner.

# GETTING KNOTTED

Can you tie a knot in a piece of string without letting either end go? I can. Try it and see if it is possible.

No luck? Then I'll tell you how to do it. First of all, place the string on a table in front of you, so it is easy to reach. Then fold your arms. Right. Now you're ready.

Keeping your arms folded, get hold of the left-hand end of the string with your right hand, and the right-hand end of the string with your left hand. Then simply unfold your arms, keeping hold of the string. Voilà – the string has a knot in it!

# PUNCTUATION PROBLEM

The sentence below illustrates the importance of correct punctuation in our language. As it is, it makes no sense at all. But properly punctuated, it makes perfect sense. Can you sort it out?

Smith where Jones had had had had had had had had had had had the examiners approval.

**Answer**

Smith, where Jones had had 'had had', had had 'had'. 'Had had' had had the examiners' approval.

SIGN IN A BAKER'S SHOP: Vienna rolls.
SCRAWLED UNDERNEATH: London swings.
*OK, so it's an old joke.*

# RIDDLE ROSTER

Tease your brain with these tantalizing riddles, and *don't* give in by looking at the answers first.

What makes a road broad?

The letter B.

What did the violin say to the guitar?

"May I string along with you?"

What's another name for a butcher's boy?

A chop assistant.

How can an unknown person get on television?

By sitting on the set.

What is filled every morning and emptied every night, except for once a year when it is filled at night and emptied in the morning?

A stocking.

On which side does a turkey have the greatest number of feathers?

The outside.

How do you make a Swiss roll?

Push him down an alp.

What do you call the life story of a car?

An autobiography.

Who sits down in front of the Queen with his hat on?

Her chauffeur.

Why can't hippopotamuses dance?

Because they have two left feet.

# EGG ON YOUR FACE

Did you know that, if you apply pressure evenly to an ordinary
hen's egg by holding it in the palm of your hand, you cannot
break it? Try it and see.

The only provisions (!) are that it must not be cracked to start
with, and you must not cheat by pressing it against a ring. Just
in case you choose a weakling, or if you are particularly strong,
it might be as well to try it over a bowl.

# EGG FLIP

Can you spin an egg and make it rise up and stand on end? Try it
and see.

Did you try it with an ordinary uncooked egg? And it failed?
Well, now try it with a hard-boiled egg and see what happens.
This time it should work. It's a good way to tease someone, if you
are the only person who knows the answer.

# RAISE YOUR GLASS

Whether your favourite tipple is wine or water, here's a little
stunt which will make people disbelieve the evidence of their
own eyes. All you do is to pick up a full glass of water (or vintage
champagne, if you prefer) and swing it over your head from one
side to the other. It will be very popular with your audience, for
they will assume (naturally enough, but wrongly, as it happens)
that you are going to get wet, and there's nothing an audience
likes better than watching a performer making a fool of himself.

However, you will neither get wet nor make a fool of yourself
if you hold the glass correctly. The way to do it is to cup your
hand around the base of the glass if it is a tumbler, or around the
bowl with the stem between your fingers if it is a wine glass. You
can then swing the glass round in a complete circle without
spilling a drop.

# HANKY PANKY

In the good old days before everyone used paper tissues, magicians used large cotton handkerchiefs in a number of clever tricks. Here are a couple you can do, using the tumbler and water from the stunt on page 20, and a man's strong cotton handkerchief.

Pour water into the tumbler until it is three-quarters full, then cover it with the handkerchief. Lift the tumbler with one hand, and tuck the ends of the handkerchief under the bottom of the tumbler with the other hand. Now hold the tumbler in the second hand, and with the first hand press the centre of the handkerchief downwards until it touches the top of the water. Then turn the tumbler upside down. Not only will the water not spill, but the handkerchief will retain its shape even when the tumbler is inverted.

For the second trick, keep the glass in the same position but draw the handkerchief up until the concave shape has been pulled taut across the mouth of the glass. The water level in the glass will fall, but the water still will not spill. If you look closely, you will see bubbles rising from the handkerchief up through the water to the top. You can proudly tell your audience that the water is boiling, for if you hold the glass near your ear, the sound of boiling will be heard. It's the only way I know of boiling water using a handkerchief!

# FAIRGROUND TRICK

If you've ever wondered how the old fairground trick with the three cups is performed, here's your answer.

Start with three cups in a row, the ones at either end facing downwards, the centre one facing upwards, like this:

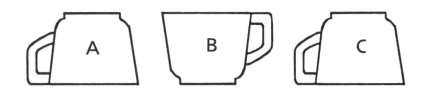

Now, in three moves, make them all face upwards, like this:

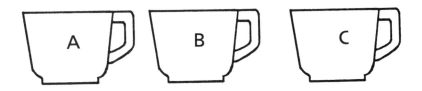

With each move, you can reverse the position of any two cups. Can you do it?

**Answer**

1. Move A and B.

2. Move A and C.

3. Move A and B.

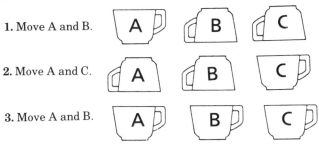

Now, if you really want to trick someone, just start off with cups A and C facing upwards, and ask a friend to make them all face upwards in three moves, moving any two cups each time. They won't be able to do it – though they may manage to end up with all the cups facing downwards.

# LEGS ELEVEN

Without stopping too long to think about it, write down this number in figures: eleven thousand, eleven hundred and eleven.

**Answer**

Did you write 11,1111? Well, you're wrong. The answer is, of course, 12,111.

# SLIPPERY CUSTOMER

Can you lift an ice-cube out of a glass of water with a piece of string? Try it and see. You might try tying the string round the ice-cube, but it will slip out. The secret is to use some salt.

Dangle the end of the string in the water and have a little salt sprinkled in the palm of your hand. After you have taken the string out of the water, hold it in your hand so that the salt adheres to it, then lay the end of the string on the ice-cube for a few moments. You will now be able to lift the ice-cube quite easily, for the salt momentarily melts the ice, which quickly freezes again and makes the end of the string adhere to it.

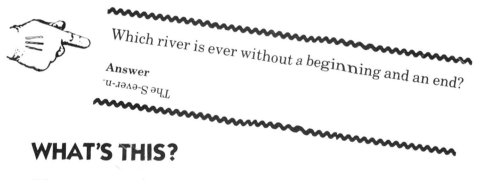

Which river is ever without a beginning and an end?

**Answer**

The S-ever-n.

# WHAT'S THIS?

What phrase does this represent?

M E
A L

**Answer**

A square meal.

# WHAT'S NEXT?

What letter comes next in this series?

O T T F F S S

**Answer**

seven.
E. They are the initial letters of the numbers one, two, three, four, five, six and

# PUZZLE PICTURE

Can you guess what this is?

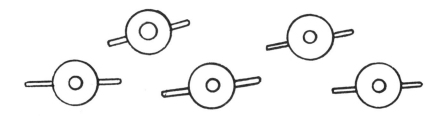

**Answer**
It's a Mexican cycle race.

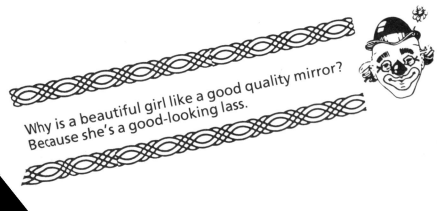

Why is a beautiful girl like a good quality mirror?
Because she's a good-looking lass.

## TONGUE TWISTER

Now see if you can stick out your tongue and touch your nose.
Can you do it, or is your tongue too short? You're not allowed to
pull at it with your hands.

   This is a good trick to play on a child, because they will try
tremendously hard. They'll also be very cross with you when you
reveal how it's done – by sticking out your tongue and touching
your nose with your hand at the same time!

## MATCHMAKING

Arrange six matches like this:

Now add five more to make nine.

**Answer:** see page 116

## HIDDEN COIN

Try making a bet with someone that you can put a £1 coin somewhere that everyone can see it but them. They won't believe you, and will cheerfully take on the bet.

Do you know where to put the coin? On the top of their head, of course!

## PAPER FOLDING

How many times do you think you can fold a piece of paper in half? Six? Sixteen? Sixty? Try it and see.

No matter how large or how small your piece of paper, or how thin it is, you will find it impossible to fold it in half more than nine times. You probably won't get further than six.

## NOW CLOSE YOUR EYES

Close your eyes. Then, keeping them closed, roll your eyeballs up as far as you can. Don't tilt your head backwards, just roll back your eyeballs. Imagine you are trying to see something above your head, then you will get into the right position. Having got into that position, try and open your eyes. You will find that you cannot! But don't panic, just stop looking upwards with your eyes closed, and you will find you can open your eyes quite easily.

# EYE, EYE!

If EYE can be turned into LID in four moves, like this:

EYE
DYE
DIE
DID
LID

by changing one letter at a time, and still making proper words, can you turn FOUR into FIVE in seven moves?

**Answer**

FIVE
FIRE
FORE
FORT
FOOT
FOOL
FOUL
FOUR

# EAR WE GO

Do you think you can write with your left ear? If you don't think so, challenge someone else to have a go. They may even go as far as sticking a pencil in their ear and bending down so their head is almost on the paper.

But it is really much more simple than that. All you do is pick up a pen or pencil and write:

## WITH MY LEFT EAR!

# FINGER MATHS

If multiplication is not your strongest point, you may like to know that there is a simple and foolproof way of multiplying by nine, by using your fingers.

Hold out your hands in front of you, palms upwards. In your mind, give each finger a number from one to ten, starting with the thumb of your left hand. Now, suppose you wanted to multiply five by nine. Count along your fingers from the left until you reach finger number five, which will be the little finger of your left hand, and bend it down towards the palm of your hand. Now count the fingers to the left of it, and those to the right of it. They are four and five respectively. And forty-five is the answer to five multiplied by nine!

If you want to multiply seven by nine, count along until you reach finger number seven, the ring finger of your right hand. There are six fingers to the left of it, and three fingers to the right of it – and the answer is sixty-three! Amazing, isn't it?

# WATERPROOF SAND

This needs a little preparation, but it is worth doing because no one will believe what they are seeing. You put a handful of sand in a bowl of water, and then scoop it out again – and it is dry!

The trick is to 'waterproof' the sand. Put some ordinary dry sand in an old pan and heat it on the stove until it is hot enough to turn a piece of white paper dropped on it brown. Add about an inch of white wax candle to it, stirring it round thoroughly until it has all mixed together with the sand. Then take the pan off the heat and leave the mixture to cool.

When it has done so, it will form a solid lump, but this can easily be crumbled up, and the resulting sand will be waterproof.

# TRIANGULATION

How many triangles are there in this drawing?

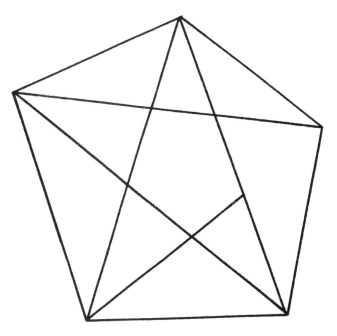

**Answer**
Thirty-five.

# WALLFLOWER

Stand with your left side against a wall, touching the wall with both your left foot and your left cheek. Now lift your right foot off the ground.

What do you mean you can't? You must be able to! Mustn't you? Strangely enough, no. Because, in order to do so you would first of all have to move slightly to the left, and you cannot do that because the wall is in your way.

# WHAT'S AFOOT?

This is a teaser to try out with someone else who has either much smaller or much larger feet than you. First, get the large-footed person to back four 'foot' lengths away from a wall. Then put an ordinary dining chair against the wall in front of them, and get them to lean over, rest their forehead against the wall above the chair, and pick it up and return to an upright position without touching the wall with their hands, arms, or anything other than their head. They will almost certainly be unable to do so, unless they are extremely strong, or the chair is extremely light.

Now get the small-footed person to try the same feat. If their feet are small enough, they will be able to do it. The trick is, of course, that they are nearer to the wall in the first place, and can operate without such long leverage and, therefore, need less strength.

# ON A TIGHTROPE

Did you know that you can make water walk a tightrope? It may sound unlikely, but it is true. This is how it is done.

First of all, you need a jug, a glass and a piece of string about a yard long. Fill the jug two-thirds full of water, and tie the string to the jug's handle. Wet the string in the jug, then stretch it across the jug's spout to the glass, about two feet away, holding the end of the string inside the glass. Raise the jug above the height of the glass, make sure the string is pulled taut, and start pouring slowly. The water will 'walk' along the string to the glass.

# MONOPOLY COMMISSION

Do you play Monopoly? If so, you will know that the denomination of the notes used in Monopoly is not the same as that in ordinary currency. So here's a little problem for Monopoly players. If Player A buys a property from Player B for £103, and pays for it with eight notes, not one of which is a £1 note, what are the eight notes with which he pays?

**Answer**
One £50 note, two £20 notes, one £5 note and four £2 notes.

# RHYME TIME

What's the beginning of eternity,
The end of time, and space;
The beginning of every end.
And the end of every race?

Well, what is it?

**Answer**
The letter E.

# PRESENT ARMS!

Try this trick for yourself or, if you want to impress a young friend by demonstrating your mysterious power over them, use them as a guinea pig.

Stand in a doorway with your arms out so you can push the backs of your hands against the door frame. You have to push fairly hard, and you have to push for a whole minute.

When the minute is up, then relax your arms, letting them fall down by your side, and step out of the doorway. Something very strange will happen. Without your wishing it, and entirely beyond your control, your arms will slowly rise up in the air! It is a most curious feeling. They will stay there for a moment or two, before relaxing again and allowing you to take control of them.

If you are trying this trick with a young friend, tell them what to do, having first explained that this will give you a mysterious power over them. Then, as they step out of the doorway, and before their arms rise up, say 'Lift up both arms!' and, of course, they will do, without realizing how or why. They will be very impressed with your powers!

# DOMINO THEORY: 1

Do you have a set of dominoes? If so, here's a teaser to really
bend your mind. From the set remove the six lowest dominoes,
i.e. the double blank, the blank/one, the blank/two, the one/one,
the one/two and the two/two. Arrange them in an equilateral
triangle, as shown in the diagram, *with each of the three sides
containing the same number of pips, and none of the joints
matching.*

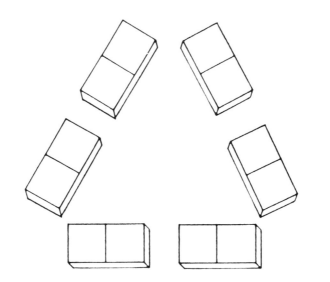

**Answer:** see page 117

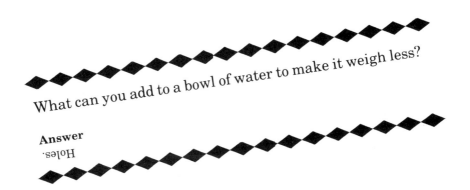

What can you add to a bowl of water to make it weigh less?

**Answer**
Holes.

# DOMINO THEORY: 2

If you found that one easy, try a harder one. This time take the
ten lowest dominoes, i.e. the six used in the previous teaser, plus
the blank/three, the one/three, the two/three and the three/
three. This time, create a square as shown below, so that the
number of pips on each side is the same but none of the joints
matches.

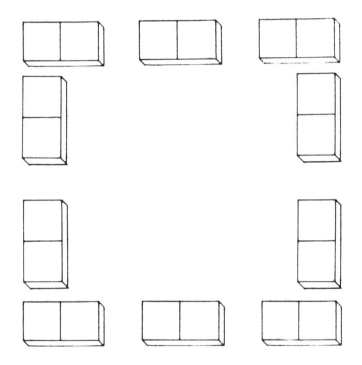

**Answer:** see page 117

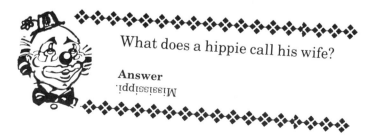

What does a hippie call his wife?

**Answer**
Mississippi.

# LETTER BOX

Which of the following rows of letters is the odd one out?

I C A C
I C A B
I C A J
I C A U
I C A Z

**Answer**
I C A Z. All the others, when read aloud, make sense, e.g. 'I see a sea', 'I see a bee'.

# LEADING QUESTION

What can you not hold for half an hour, even though it is lighter than a feather?

**Answer**
Your breath.

# THE LEAPING BRICK

Look at this drawing of a brick. Stare at it for a moment, close your eyes and then look at it again. What happens? Try staring at it and blinking once or twice to see what happens then.

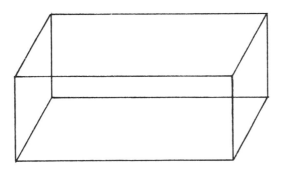

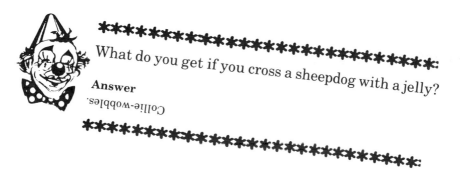

What do you get if you cross a sheepdog with a jelly?

**Answer**
Collie-wobbles.

37

## MAKING ENDS MEET

How good is your co-ordination? Find out with this little test. Take two newly-sharpened pencils and hold one in each hand, about two feet apart, with the points of the pencils facing each other. Now move them together to get the two points to meet exactly in the centre.

Did you find it easy? If so, try doing it with one eye closed. I bet you can't do it the first time now! In fact, it is very difficult because we need to see with both eyes together in order to be able to judge distances correctly.

What's a Hindu?

**Answer**
Lays iggs.

# WHAT A CARD!

How many sides has a playing card? I can hear you thinking I must be stupid, for everyone knows that it has two sides. Ah, but I can show you a playing card with four sides.

Look. Here is the ace of hearts.

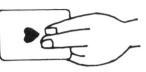

On its other side is the four of hearts.

On its third side is the three of hearts.

And on its fourth side is the six of hearts!

It is, of course, a trick – but a very effective one, if you hold the card exactly as shown in the illustrations. You will need a bit of practice in turning the card round, but once you have mastered that, then you are guaranteed to fool people.

This is how it is done. One side of the card looks like this:

And the other like this:

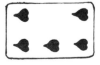

# THE LAST COIN

I'm going to let you into a little secret – how to always win in a game. You need two players and twenty coins (or counters, if you're afraid of losing).

The idea is to scatter the coins on a table and take turns to pick up one, two or three at a time. The player who picks up the last coin is the winner.

If you want to be sure of winning, then politely let your opponent go first. The trick is to note how many coins he takes each time, and to subtract that number from four. The answer will be the number of coins that you must now pick up. Supposing your opponent picks up one coin, you must then pick up three. If he picks up two, you pick up two, and so on. By the time your opponent is about to start his fifth go, there will only be four coins left, and since he cannot pick up more than three at a time, you cannot fail to win.

# SPOONING

Here's a very silly trick which will make people laugh. It is hanging a spoon from the end of your nose.

The way to do it is to warm the bowl of the spoon first, tilt your head back and guide the spoon slowly down your nose, until it comes to rest with the bowl on the end of your nose and the handle hanging down towards your mouth. Slowly return your head to its normal position, and, with a bit of luck, the spoon will remain hanging from your nose. You may need to practise a couple of times to get it right.

# ABSOLUTELY LOOPY

Here is an amazing phenomenon, which can be demonstrated with a strip of paper about one foot long and two inches wide, a piece of sticky tape, a pencil and a pair of scissors.

First of all, cut out a strip of paper, give it one twist, and then stick the ends together with a bit of tape. The loop you have made has some amazing properties. For a start, it only has one side, not two, as you can apparently see. You can demonstrate this by starting at the join and running a pencil line all the way along the centre of the strip. Without lifting the pencil from the paper, you will be able to go all the way round, back to the join, and if you look at the paper you will discover that the line appears on *both* sides – thus proving that the loop has only one side.

Right. Now cut along the line you have drawn to divide your loop into two loops. And what happens? You end up with one extra-large loop. Repeat the same procedure with your large loop – cutting along it lengthwise – to get an even larger loop. But it doesn't work this time, does it? It makes two loops instead!

# VANISHING TRICK

Now I'll tell you how to do a real-life magic trick, by making a pen disappear. You will need a ballpoint pen with a cap, a sheet of paper, a length of fine elastic and a safety pin.

Say to your audience 'Here I have a ballpoint pen and a piece of paper. Will you sign your name on the paper? Right. Now I'm going to roll the pen up inside the paper, and twist the end so it doesn't fall out. You can feel the pen here. Right. Now I'll twist the other end. Now watch very carefully. I'm going to tear the paper in half – and, voilà, the pen has disappeared!'

It's a good trick, isn't it? This is how it's done. One end of the elastic is attached to the cap of the pen, and the other end of the elastic is tied to the safety pin which is pinned to the inside of your sleeve, so the pen cap hangs just below your elbow.

Before you offer the pen to someone take hold of the cap, and keep hold of it while you are offering them the pen, making sure it doesn't shoot up your sleeve. As the member of your audience actually uses the pen, they will not suspect that it has been tampered with. Now, take the pen back, put the cap on it and roll it in the paper to make a tube, letting the person feel the pen in the far end of the tube. Then you let the pen shoot up the inside of your sleeve. Turn the tube round and twist the other end so that it looks as if the pen is still inside it . . . and just to prove that the pen has vanished you can then tear the tube in half.

# LETTERALLY

If you are clever, you might manage to do this conundrum in your head, but lesser mortals might have to succumb to using a pencil and a piece of paper.

Think of all the letters of the alphabet.

Take away the second.

Take away the twenty-second.

Take away the onc that comes before the previous one you took away.

Take away the letter O, and the letter that comes after the letter that comes after O.

Take away the sixth, fifth and fourth letters.

Take away X, Y, and Z.

Take away the third letter.

Add Q.

Take away T.

Take away the seventh letter.

Add the last letter.

Take away H, and the letter that comes seven places before it.

Take away the letter that comes before R.

Add the letter that follows P.

Take away R and P.

Take away the remaining vowel.

Take away the three letters that follow it.

Take away N and the letter that comes before it.

Take away the last letter of the alphabet.

Take away all the consonants in the word 'sew'.

What letter is left?

43

# LIGHT TOUCH

Here's a trick that proves you can cut with light. You need a bottle with a cork, a piece of bent wire, a small weight, a piece of cotton, a magnifying glass – and a sunny day. The last is probably the most difficult to acquire.

Twist the wire into the shape of a hook and press it into the cork. Tie the cotton round the hook, and tie the other end of the cotton to the weight. Then put the cork in the bottle, with the weight suspended above the bottom of the bottle.

The trick is now to cut the cotton without removing the cork from the bottle – which sounds impossible, unless you have a magnifying glass. This is held so that it focuses the sun's rays on to the cotton – and in a few moments the heat will burn right through it.

★ ★ ★ ★ ★ ★ ★ ★ ★ ★ ★ ★ ★ ★ ★ ★

What kind of animal would you like to be on a bleak January day?

A little otter.

★ ★ ★ ★ ★ ★ ★ ★ ★ ★ ★ ★ ★ ★

# PINT SIZE

If you have a three-pint jug and a five-pint jug, and nothing else to help you, how can you measure out exactly one pint of water?

**Answer**

First fill the three-pint jug, then empty the water from it into the five-pint jug. Fill the three-pint jug again, and empty as much as you can from it into the five-pint jug. You will be left with exactly one pint of water in the three-pint jug.

# TRICK OF THE CAMERA

Trick photography is great fun to do. Here is one simple stunt, for which you need two models and a camera.

Get the first model to stand near the camera with her arm held stretched out to the side, and her palm held upwards, as if holding something. Then get the other model to stand well behind the first, and in line with her outstretched hand. Line them up in the viewfinder so it appears that the further model is standing on the nearer model's hand – and take the picture. The only problem is that you won't be able to see how the trick has worked until the film is developed.

## TAKE THE CHAIR

Sit down in an ordinary straight-backed chair, without arms. Put your feet flat on the floor and keep your back straight against the back of the chair. Fold your arms across your chest, and just sit there for a while.

Now, without leaning forward, or lifting your feet off the floor, try and stand up. Can you do it? Unless you have enormously strong muscles, you won't be able to. Unless you move your body forwards, or your feet back under the chair, you may just sit there for ever!

# NON-BURSTING BALLOON

Can you stick a pin in a balloon without bursting it? I can. There is, of course, a trick involved.

What you have to do is to stick a small piece of transparent tape over part of the balloon, and stick the pin in there. You can stick the pin right through the balloon, but it will not burst or pop. It will, apparently, not have been pierced at all. In time it will deflate as air escapes through the tiny pin-hole – but you will have stuck a pin in it without bursting it.

# CARD TRICK

Lying on the table are three playing cards. A diamond is on the left of a spade, though not necessarily next to it; an eight is on the right of a king; a ten is on the left of a heart; and a heart is on the left of a spade. What are the three cards?

**Answer**

The ten of diamonds, the king of hearts and the eight of spades.

# BUDDING ARTISTS

Mrs Palette has a number of artistic nieces and nephews, so at Christmas she goes into an art suppliers to buy presents for them. She discovers that she can buy three boxes of coloured chalks plus one box of coloured pencils for the same price as two boxes of paints. And one box of coloured chalks, two boxes of coloured pencils and three boxes of paints would cost her a total of £25.

How much each are boxes of chalks, boxes of pencils and boxes of paints?

**Answer**

£2, £4 and £5 respectively.

# STRANGE SENTENCE

Can you spot anything unusual about this sentence?
   Ten animals I slam in a net.

**Answer**

It is a palindrome, i.e. it reads the same backwards as forwards.

# STRENGTH OF TEN

There is a way of proving that you have the strength of ten
people. If you don't believe it, then all you have to do is to gather
up to ten friends and try it out.

Stand facing a wall and, with your arms stretched out
straight, lean on it with your hands. Your palms should be flat,
and the fingers should be facing upwards. Now ask someone to
stand behind you in a similar posture, with his or her hands
resting on your shoulders. Then get someone to stand behind
him or her, and so on, until you have up to ten people behind
you.

At a given signal, get them all to push towards you with all
their strength, while you in turn brace yourself against the wall
and resist them. Surprisingly, you will not be crushed by their
weight. In fact, you should be able to withstand them easily as
each person absorbs the forward push of the person behind them.
So as long as you can withstand the person directly behind you,
you will be all right. If you have any doubts about the matter,
don't put anyone too heavy right behind you!

# ALL-ENVELOPING

Here is a picture of an envelope. It might have contained an invitation to Aunty Ida's birthday party, to Clarrie's wedding, or simply the gas bill. The puzzle is to copy the drawing exactly, without taking your pencil off the page and without going over the same line twice.

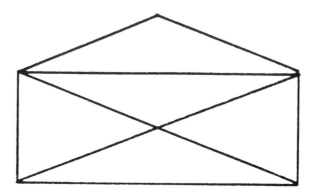

**Answer:** see page 118

# RUNNERS

If Mary can run 4.12 kilometres in an hour, and Maureen can run a kilometre in 4.12 minutes, who is the faster runner?

**Answer**
Maureen.

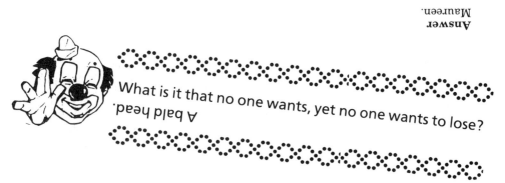

What is it that no one wants, yet no one wants to lose?
A bald head.

# TEARING OFF A STRIP

This stunt looks very easy, but try it before you decide that it is. Take an A4 sheet of paper and make two cuts in it, as shown in the illustration. Then, holding the two outer pieces at their upper, uncut ends try, by giving a single sharp pull, to tear the paper completely so you end up with three separate pieces. Can you do it?

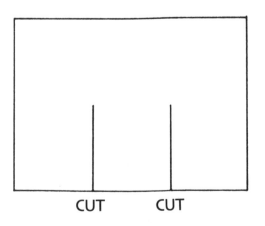

CUT    CUT

# BROKEN NOSE

Do you know the old trick of breaking your nose? Old it may be, but it never fails to amuse a child. This is how you do it.

Cup your hands over your nose and put your thumbs in your mouth. This should be hidden from the front by your hands. Rest your thumbnails against your two front teeth. Then all you do is to bend your hands from side to side, as if you are breaking your nose and, to prove it, you make cracking sounds by snapping your thumbnails against your top teeth. Your young audience will be amazed when you remove your hands from your nose and prove you have also managed to restore it to health!

# KNIFE EDGE

Can you pick up a knife? Of course you can. Can you lift five knives at the same time? I expect you think you can do that too. But there's a catch, of course. The trick is to lift four knives with a fifth. Can you do that?

**Answer:** see page 118

50

# CATS AND MICE

Here are three cats and three mice. In three moves, rearrange them so that all the cats are together on the left, and all the mice together on the right.

**Answer:** see page 119

# BALANCING TRICK

I don't know why this trick works, but it does, and it is very impressive. Bend a wire coat hanger into a diamond shape, hold it upside down and balance a 2p piece on the end of the hook. Then swing it round in a circle without the 2p falling off. It sounds impossible, but it's easy with a bit of practice.

☆ ☆ ☆ ☆ ☆ ☆ ☆ ☆ ☆ ☆
How do you make notes out of stone?

**Answer**
By rearranging the letters.

☆ ☆ ☆ ☆ ☆ ☆ ☆ ☆ ☆ ☆

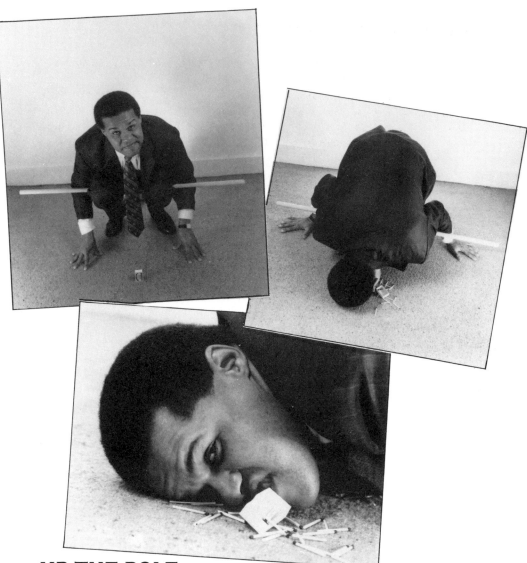

## UP THE POLE

This is a test of balance that requires a broomstick or pole of some kind, and a small item, such as a matchbox, pencil sharpener, etc. Crouch down with the pole behind your knees, put your arms around the pole (you'll feel like a trussed chicken by this time), and your hands on the ground in front of you. The small object, such as the matchbox, should be on the ground in front of you.

Now, the challenge is to lean forwards and pick up the object in your teeth, without overbalancing.

# REVOLVING CROSS

Fill a wine glass with water almost to the top, but make sure that the rim and sides of the glass are dry.

Then cut a cross out of paper, so that the ends are long enough to fold over the sides of the glass without it slipping off. If you now hold the base of the glass with one hand, and with the other hand rub the tip of one finger on any part of the glass that lies between two arms of the cross, the cross will move. If you rub right round the glass, the cross will revolve in a complete circle.

# LEWIS CARROLL'S CLOCKS

Lewis Carroll, the famous author of *Alice in Wonderland* and *Through the Looking Glass*, also created mind-boggling brainteasers. Here is one of them. Can you solve it?

I have two clocks. One has stopped completely. The other gains half a minute every twenty-four hours. Which of the two clocks tells the correct time more often?

**Answer**
The clock that has stopped.

What kind of umbrella does Joan Collins carry on a rainy day?
A wet one.

# WATERPROOF POSTCARD

Did you know that picture postcards are waterproof? Here's a way to prove it. Fill a tumbler with water, then put the card, picture side down, on top of it. Now be courageous and turn it over. Amazingly, the postcard will hold the water in place without any spillage.

You can use this trick to win a bet. Wager someone they cannot pick up a glass filled with water without spilling it. Prepare the glass and card as above, put your hand under the card, and lower the glass to a table, putting it down very carefully upside down. Slide the card out gently. Provided the glass is not moved, no water will spill. But your friend will not be able to lift up the glass without spilling the water!

# PAPER BRIDGE

If you stand two glasses 6 inches apart, did you know that you can make a bridge between them with a piece of paper and stand a third glass on it?

Before you try it, there's just one small point to explain. The paper bridge has to be pleated, concertina-fashion, or it will not work.

## SOLDIERING ON

If a soldier is facing west, and is given the instructions: 'Right
turn! About turn! Left turn!' in which direction will he be facing?

**Answer**

East.

# 1089

No, this isn't a history lesson, but an odd number phenomenon.
Choose any three digits from 0 to 9 and write them down. Then
reverse the digits and write down the new number. Subtract the
lower number of the two from the higher.

Look at your answer, reverse its digits, and add the reversed
number to the answer. The result will be 1089, whatever three
digits you chose originally.

Here is an example.

```
   523
−  325
  ————
   198
```

```
   198
+  891
  ————
  1089
```

# HANDICRAFT

If you were a carpenter, could you make this wooden triangle?

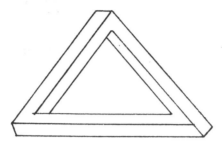

**Answer**
˙oN

## UNDER WATER

I bet you I can sing under water. Don't you believe me? It's a sneaky trick to play on someone, but it is one you can always win if you know the secret. Simply fill a glass of water, hold it over your head, and sing!

# BIG IDEAS

If a housefly were to be enlarged 1,000,000,000 times, would it be approximately the size of an apple, as large as the Empire State Building, as large as Mount Kilimanjaro, or as large as the moon?

**Answer**

Approximately as large as the moon.

# MONKEY BUSINESS

Put ten matches on a table and make a monkey out of them.

**Answer:** see page 119

# ALPHABET

How many letters are there in the alphabet? Did I hear you answer twenty-six? Well, you're wrong. There are eleven – three in 'the' and eight in 'alphabet'!

How does one angel greet another?

**Answer**

'Halo.'

# GREEDY GUTS

Try this trick on a child.

YOU: Where's my chocolate biscuit? Have you eaten it?

CHILD: No.

YOU: Are you sure?

CHILD: Of course I'm sure.

YOU: Well, never mind. Let's play a game. I'll start by saying 'I one it', and you say 'I two it', then I'll say 'I three it', and so on.

CHILD: OK.

YOU: I one it.

CHILD: I two it.

YOU: I three it.

CHILD: I four it.

YOU: I five it.

CHILD: I six it.

YOU: I seven it.

CHILD: I eight it.

YOU: Just as I thought, you greedy guts!

# THE LAST STRAW

This is a mean trick to play, but it is rather a clever one. Make two small holes in each end of an ordinary drinking straw, about half an inch from the end. To use the straw, cover the two top holes (which will be invisible at a quick glance) with your fingers. If you then offer the drink to someone else, they will not notice the holes, and will be quite mystified as to why they cannot suck any liquid up the straw.

# QUITE A JAR

Do you think you are strong enough to pull a polythene bag out of an empty jar with your bare hands? Of course you do. Well, try it and see.

Use a jar with a neck wide enough to get your hand inside. Put the polythene bag inside it and fasten it round the neck of the jar with a rubber band. Now try and pull it out.

Strangely enough, you will find that you cannot do so. This is because the rubber band creates an airtight seal, and your hand is having to struggle against the pressure of the air, not the weight of the bag.

# AN ARM AND A LEG

Sit at a desk with a sheet of paper and a pencil in front of you.
Now write the word 'continuously' on the sheet of paper. But
while you are doing it, imagine the big toe of your right foot, if
you are right-handed, or of your left foot, if you are left-handed,
drawing a large imaginary circle on the floor, and move it round
as if it were doing so.

It's ten to one that you will either stop writing, or stop moving
your foot. You won't be able to do both simultaneously.

# FISTICUFFS

If you ask someone to make
fists of both their hands, and
then sit one fist upon another,
pressing them together as
hard as they can, do you think
you could separate the fists
using just your fingertips? Try
hitting one fist with your right
index finger and one with your
left index finger, and you will
be able to knock them
sideways quite easily.

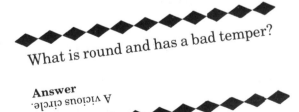

What is round and has a bad temper?

**Answer**
A vicious circle.

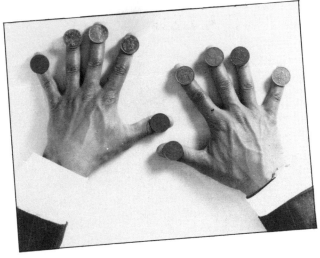

## HANDFULS OF MONEY

Find ten 1p or 2p coins. Lay your left hand palm downwards on a table, and balance one of the coins on each of your fingers, between the nail and the first joint. Now comes the difficult bit. Try getting the other five coins balanced in the same way on the fingers of your right hand without losing those on your left! PS The easiest way is to put them in a row at the edge of a table and slide them on to your fingers.

## HOT AND COLD

Can you tell hot water from cold water by immersing your hands in it? Of course you can. Are you sure? Just to make absolutely certain, try this experiment.

Fill three bowls with water. One should be filled with cold water, one with water as hot as the hand can bear, and the third with lukewarm water. Immerse your right hand in the bowl of cold water, and your left hand in the bowl of hot, and keep them there for two or three minutes. (This seems a long time, so it is best to count or time it.) Then take both hands out and put them at the same time into the bowl of lukewarm water, and see if you can tell whether it is hot or cold.

It's strange, isn't it? The water will feel hot to your right hand, and cold to your left. Now are you so sure you can tell hot from cold?

# HAND STAND

Can you eat a biscuit while standing on one hand? You have to take care not to choke on the crumbs, naturally. What? You are not young or athletic enough to stand on one hand? Are you sure? Because, in fact, anyone can do it. Really they can.

Simply crouch down, with your biscuit in one hand, and place one of your feet very carefully on your other hand. Now eat the biscuit. Simple, isn't it?

# VANISHING COIN

Did you know that you can make a coin disappear from under a glass by putting a plate or saucer over the top of the glass? Try it and see. Fill a glass with water, and place it carefully over a coin. You will, of course, be able to see the coin through the glass and through the water. Now cover the top of the glass with a plate or saucer – and you will discover that the coin has disappeared. This is because you can only see the coin from above, and the plate has blocked your view.

If you take away the plate, and look at the surface of the water level in the glass from the side, another odd thing will happen. The coin will look as if it is floating on the water, not underneath it.

# 100 UP

This is a game for two players which, if you know the trick, you can be sure of winning. The players take it in turns to choose a number between one and ten and add them on to the previous total. The winner is the one who reaches 100 first. This is how you win. You make sure that you are the player who reaches twelve first. And then you make sure that you reach twenty-three first, then thirty-four, then forty-five, then fifty-six, then sixty-seven, then seventy-eight, then eighty-nine. Thus if you reach eighty-nine first, you can make your opponent reach ninety-nine, after which the only number you can add is one, meaning that you have reached 100 first and have, therefore, won.

# WHAT?

What is always in front of you, though you can never see it?

What occurs four times in every week, twice in every month, but only once in a year?

What goes from London to Bristol without moving?

What lives on its own substance, but dies the moment it has devoured itself?

**Answers**

A candle.
The M4 motorway.
The letter E.
Your future.

What did Cinderella say when her photographs didn't arrive?
'Some day my prints will come.'

# I BEG YOUR PARDON

**A slight inclination of the cranium is as adequate as a spasmodic movement of one optic to an equine quadruped utterly devoid of any visionary capacity.**

What does this mean in plain English?

**Answer**

A nod is as good as a wink to a blind horse.

# SQUARE BASHING

Can you divide this rectangle into five parts to form a perfect square?

**Answer:** see page 119

# PAPER PUZZLE

If I waved an ordinary, A4-sized piece of paper at you, and told you that I was going to cut a hole in it with a pair of scissors, big enough for me to climb through, would you think it was possible? How would I do it?

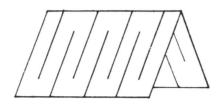

**Answer**

The secret is to fold it in half and cut alternately from each side, though not all the way across. Now the paper can be unfolded. Cut along the fold, leaving the ends uncut, to make a large loop through which an adult can climb easily.

# TOP SPIN

If you take a coin with a milled edge, such as a 5p or a 10p piece, and hold it between the points of two pins, you can make it spin by blowing on it. Try it and see.

# ELBOW ROOM

This trick will test your reflexes, and is very impressive if you get it right.

Hold your arm as shown in the photograph, and place a pile of coins on your elbow. It is best if all the coins are the same, so they will balance better.

Then the idea is to bring your hand down as quickly as you can, and catch the pile of coins before they fall. It sounds impossible but, although it may take a bit of practice, it *can* be done.

# HOUSE OF CARDS

Making a house of cards is a favourite trick, but it is not easy to do. The first tip is to choose a surface which is not too slippery, or the whole thing will fall down almost before you have started. The secret is to prop the cards against each other to make a letter M, then put a card across the top. You then start the next M on top of it, like this.

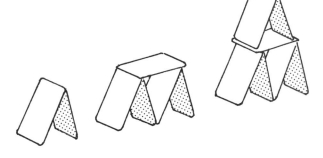

# PREDICTABLE

It is quite possible to predict what someone is going to say next. All you have to do is to say to them, 'I know exactly what you are going to say next.'

They will reply, 'What?'

And you can simply show them the word 'what' scribbled on a piece of paper – because it is ten to one that that is what they will say.

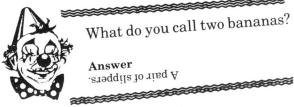

What do you call two bananas?

**Answer**
A pair of slippers.

# STRONG FINGER

Did you know that your little finger is strong enough to hold someone down in a chair?

Get someone to sit in a chair with their head tilted back and their chin up. Put your little finger against their forehead, and ask them to try and stand up. Surprisingly, unless they try to cheat by wriggling to one side, they will be quite unable to stand. This is because, before they stand, they have to move their head forwards, and your little finger will be strong enough to prevent that movement.

# SCRAMBLED BRAIN

Can you make any sense out of this sentence?

*Brain trouble with no a brainy has teasers tough brain.*

**Answer**

A brainy brain has no trouble with tough brain teasers.

# CAREER GIRLS

Molly, Milly and Mandy were three sisters, each of whom was about to set out upon a new career in a different city. From the following facts, can you work out who was going to do what and where?

One was a teacher who was going to work in Bristol.
Mandy was not going to work in London.
The Manchester-bound sister was not Milly.
Molly was a nurse.
The secretary was going to work in London.

**Answer**

Molly was a nurse going to work in Manchester.
Milly was a secretary going to work in London.
Mandy was a teacher going to work in Bristol.

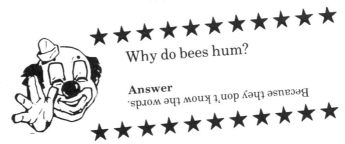

★ ★ ★ ★ ★ ★ ★ ★ ★ ★ ★ ★

Why do bees hum?

**Answer**
Because they don't know the words.

★ ★ ★ ★ ★ ★ ★ ★ ★ ★ ★ ★

# TONGUE TIED

Next time you have a few minutes to spare, have a go at getting your tongue round these teasing twisters. If you do happen to find any of them easy, then repeat it ten times without stopping, and see if it is still easy. (The first one is a good test of this.)

Red lorry, yellow lorry.

The Leith police dismisseth us.

The chased treasure chest's thrice chipped.

Thistle-sifters sift thistles in the thistle fields.

Nat's knapsack strap's snapped.

That bloke's back brake-block's broke.

High roller, low roller, lower a roller.

A truly frugal rural ruler's mural.

# UNIQUE WORD

There is one word in English which, if written in capital letters, reads the same upside down as it does the right way up. What is it?

**Answer**
NOON

# QUITE A HANDFUL

Have you got large, strong hands? If so, you will easily be able to crumple a double-page spread from a broadsheet newspaper with one hand, won't you?

Have a go. Don't cheat and use the other hand, just see if you can crumple the sheet into a ball with one hand alone. The chances are that unless you have extremely large hands you will not be able to do it.

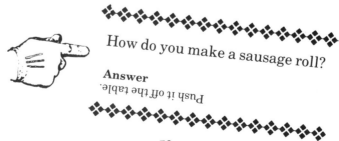

How do you make a sausage roll?

**Answer**
Push it off the table.

# LEAPING RUBBER BAND

Do you know how to make an ordinary rubber band leap from one finger to the next? Try hanging one from the index finger of your left hand. Then take hold of the other end of the band in your right hand, and separate its strands so one is in front of the other. Then wrap the band round your middle finger, taking it underneath first and then bringing it back over the top, keeping the strands apart. When you have done this, slip the end of the band back on to the end of your index finger. The two fingers are now fastened together.

Now get hold of your index finger with your right hand and bend your middle finger. The rubber band will leap from your index finger to hang on your middle finger. It's a simple trick, but great fun to do.

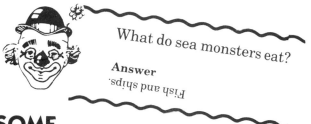

What do sea monsters eat?

**Answer**
Fish and ships.

# TOOTHSOME

Younger members of the family will love this trick. All they will need is an orange, and a knife, if they are old enough to use one. If not, you will have to use it for them.

Cut the orange into quarters, then carefully peel one quarter. The idea is then to make some hideous orange 'false teeth' with which they can alarm everyone. Just cut two jagged edges, like this:

The little monster only has to wedge one piece of peel under his top lip, and the other under his lower lip, and quietly keep his mouth closed until someone looks at him or speaks. A slow smile in reply should do the trick!

# BLACK-LISTED

This is another trick the youngsters will love. It is a spoken word game that goes like this:

YOU: I bet I can make you say the word 'black'.
CHILD: I bet you can't.
YOU: I bet you twenty chocolate bars I can.
CHILD: OK. Try.
YOU: What are the colours of the Union Jack?
CHILD: Red, white and blue.
YOU: There you are! I told you I'd make you say 'blue'.
CHILD: No, you didn't, you said you'd make me say 'black'.
YOU: You just did! I think I've won the bet!

## JUMP TO IT

I can put a book somewhere on the floor of any room where no one else will be able to jump over it. Can you?

**Answer**

You can, if you put it in the corner of the room.

# BIG MEDICINE

Say to a child, 'I can turn you into an Indian chief'.

He or she will reply, 'How?'

Whereupon you say, 'See, I've started already!'

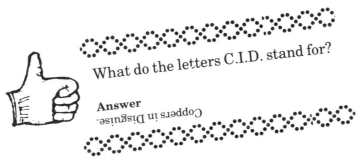

What do the letters C.I.D. stand for?

**Answer**
Coppers in Disguise.

# UNDER THE INFLUENCE

Get someone to clasp their hands together, so that the thumbs are crossed and the two index fingers are extended upwards, but held apart from each other.

Say you are going to make his or her index fingers move together, whether they want them to or not. Then wave your hands around, and mutter some mumbo jumbo, and, lo and behold, the fingers will move together! The fact is, of course, that the fingers get tired held in that position and automatically move towards each other, regardless of what you do about it!

# I SAY!

This teaser is so obvious it is amazing how many people fall for it. All you do is to give your friends a piece of paper and a pencil, and bet them they can't write a small letter 'I' with a dot over it ...and the chances are, they won't be able to. Most people write this:

Whereas the answer is, of course, this:

# SO TIRED

For some reason, yawning is highly infectious. Have you noticed? Next time you are in a crowded room, try giving a gentle yawn or two and see what happens. Soon everyone else will be yawning too. I have known this to work even with dogs, though not with cats!

# SHEEPISH

What is unusual about this verse?

Mary had a tiny lamb,
Its coat was light as snow;
And all around, as Mary ran,
Her lamb would run also.

**Answer**

It does not contain the letter E, the most common letter in the English language.

# WHAT NEXT?

Which number comes next in this series?

1, 2, 5, 10, 20, 50, 1, 5?

**Answer**

10. They are the denominations of coins and notes in sterling currency.

# FEAT OF STRENGTH

Lie flat on your back on the floor with your arms folded across your chest. Can you stand up keeping your arms in that position?

## FINGER CONTROL

Hold out your hands in front of you with the index fingers pointing towards each other. Now slowly rotate the tip of your right index finger in a clockwise direction. Then slowly rotate the tip of the left index finger in an anticlockwise direction. That's not difficult, is it? Now try and rotate both fingertips simultaneously in opposite directions. If you can do *that,* then your co-ordination is superb!

What do you call an airline pilot who is also a magician?

**Answer**
A flying saucerer.

## SILLY JUMP

Clasp your hands together in front of your body to make a loop. Can you jump through it with both feet?

## BUTTON IT

A silly but effective trick can be played like this. Bet someone they can't button up their coat in less than a minute. It sounds very easy, doesn't it? But the point is that most people start by buttoning their coat at the top, working downwards, rather than at the bottom, working upwards, so strictly speaking they are not buttoning *up* their coat at all!

# TRIANGLES GALORE

If you draw seven straight lines like this, you can produce six triangles, none of which overlaps another. But it is possible, by drawing seven straight lines, to produce eleven triangles, none of which overlaps another. Can you do it?

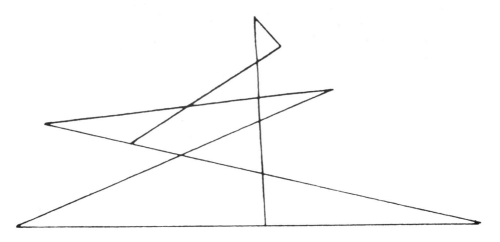

**Answer:** see page 120

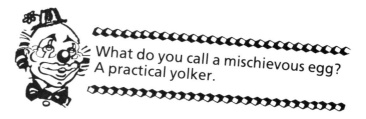

What do you call a mischievous egg? A practical yolker.

# CONSTANT CRY

If each of these letters represents a digit, can you work out the sum?

```
  S E N D
  M O R E +
M O N E Y
```

**Answer**
```
  9 5 6 7
  1 0 8 5 +
1 0 6 5 2
```

## CUSHY NUMBER

Can you lie flat on the floor on
your back, pick up a cushion
with your feet, lift it over your
head and drop it on the floor
behind you?

# EGG-STRAORDINARY

This trick has to be prepared in advance, but it is guaranteed to
mystify everybody. It requires a small egg, an empty milk
bottle, and some vinegar.

The egg should be small enough to slip inside the bottle. Once
it is in there, pour on it enough vinegar to cover it and leave it
for twenty-four hours. Then pour away the vinegar, and rinse
out the bottle with cold water to kill the vinegar smell. Don't
worry, you will not be able to wash out the egg, for it will have
become much larger – too large to get it out of the bottle. People
will be mystified as to how it got there, and you can invent
whatever unlikely story you wish to explain its presence!

# KNOCK, KNOCK

Here's a challenge and a half.
Can you knock a glass of water
on the ground without spilling
a drop?

**Answer**

All you need to do is to put the glass on the ground, lift it, and tap it gently on the
ground once or twice.

## CLASSIC CO-ORDINATION TEST

This is a well-known test, but it doesn't make it any easier to do.
All you have to do is to put one hand on your stomach, and move
it round in small circles, while tapping your head with the other
hand. You will find that either both hands move in circles, or
both hands tap, unless your co-ordination is extremely good.

# THE GREAT ESCAPOLOGISTS

A very impressive yet simple trick, this needs two people to perform it, and an audience to impress. It also requires two lengths of rope or string, each about a yard long.

You get someone to tie the wrists of yourself and your partner as shown in the illustration. You then say 'My partner and myself are tied together, as you can see. You can examine the rope and the knots. It is impossible for us to escape. And yet …Abracadabra – we've done it!'

The secret is to stand with your left side facing the audience. You move your hands slowly to conceal what you are about to do. With your right hand you get hold of the loop which is tied to your partner's wrist, bring it to the inside of your own left wrist, tuck it under the rope there, and into the palm of your left hand. Push the loop through, pass it over the fingers of your left hand, and you will be released.

# BOTTLE ON A ROPE

Can you hold a bottle by a piece of rope in its neck? It's easy when you know how. All you need is a small eraser, preferably one with rounded edges.

First of all you push the eraser into the bottle. If you use a coloured bottle no one will see it. Insert the rope into the neck of the bottle and turn the bottle upside down. This will ensure that the eraser falls into the neck of the bottle, trapping the end of the rope. When you turn the bottle over, if you do not shake it about, the eraser will remain in position, with the bottle apparently hanging from the end of the rope.

Where did Noah keep his bees?

**Answer**
In the ark-hives.

# WATER INTO WINE

Being able to turn water into wine is something we would all like to do. But once you know the secret, it is quite easy. There is a snag, though – you do need some wine to start with.

With your audience in front of you pour some water into a large jug. Then you say 'What a pity it isn't wine, but maybe if I wave a magic wand over it, it will turn into wine.' This you do, then pour out a glass of wine from the jug!

The secret is to hide a plastic drinking cup full of wine inside the jug, packed around with pieces of sponge or absorbent cloths. These absorb the water you pour into the jug. Once it has been absorbed, if you tip up the jug you can pour the wine out of the plastic cup hidden in the jug into a glass. If the plastic cup slips, stick it to the base of the jug with some blobs of Blu-tack.

# VERSE PUZZLE

The blanks in this poem can all be filled in by words composed of the same four letters, though each word is different. Can you work out what they are?

No ---- was there with cheerful light;
The ---- raced round the ship all night;
With ---- and wiles the sailors sought;
But by the ---- not one was caught.

**Answer**

Star, rats, arts, tars.

# CHANGING COLOUR

Here is a party trick with which to delight young children. You need a number of balloons, half of which are white, and half of which are yellow. (Or any other colours you prefer). You also need a drawing pin and some Blu-tack.

Hide the yellow balloons inside the white ones. Blow up the yellow balloons and tie them up, then blow up the white balloons to a slightly larger size (they will have inflated anyway, being outside the yellow ones), and tie them up.

You can then say to your young audience 'What a pity it is that the plain white balloons aren't pretty yellow ones.' As you do so, one by one give the white balloons a surreptitious jab with the drawing pin, which you have stuck on your thumb with a blob of Blu-tack. They will burst, to reveal the bright yellow balloons underneath, as if by magic.

84

# TWO-FACED

It is great fun to create a face that looks the same upside down as the right way up. The way to do it is to ensure that the ears and eyes are about halfway down the face, that the nose sticks up above the eyes as well as going below them, and that you create features such as a mouth that can also look like a crease in the forehead. A moustache makes it easy, too, for it becomes eyebrows when the face is turned upside down. Here is one way of doing it.

# HOW MANY Ts?

One of the longest words in the dictionary is ANTIDISESTABLISHMENTARIANISM. How many Ts in that?

**Answer**

Two – one at the beginning and one at the end (of 'that', of course!)

# PRACTICAL YOLKING

Say to a young friend: How do you spell the word 'joke'?
He or she will reply: J, O, K, E.
You: How do you spell the word 'folk'?
Friend: F, O, L, K.
You: How do you spell the word 'poke'?
Friend: P, O, K, E.
You: How do you spell the white of an egg?
Friend: Y, O, L, K.
You: No, that's the yellow part of an egg!

# PALMING A GLASS

If you hold out your hand with the palm downwards you can lift
a glass full of water with it!

It looks impossible, but it works! Fill the glass to the brim and
stand it on a level surface. Put the palm of your hand over it
with the fingers bent down almost to a right angle, then press
your palm on to the rim and raise your fingers quickly until they
are horizontal and your palm is fully stretched out. You should
then be able to lift the glass, because you have created a partial
vacuum between the surface of the water and your palm.

# FATHER AND SON

The ages of a father and his son are the same when the digits are reversed. A year ago, the father was twice as old as the son. How old are they both now?

**Answer**

73 and 37.

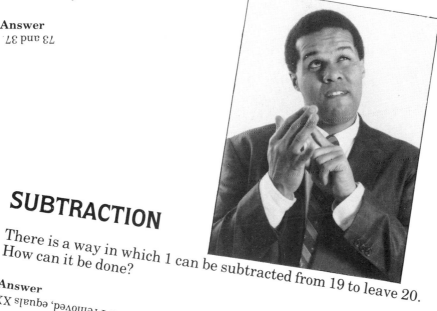

# SUBTRACTION

There is a way in which 1 can be subtracted from 19 to leave 20. How can it be done?

**Answer**

By using roman numerals, XIX, with 1 removed, equals XX.

# WORD GAMES

Here are a couple of word games with which to tease and delight a child.

### Remember Me

YOU: Will you remember me in twenty year's time?
CHILD: Of course I will.
YOU: Will you remember me in ten year's time?
CHILD: Yes.
YOU: Will you remember me in five year's time?
CHILD: Yes.
YOU: Will you remember me in one year's time?
CHILD: Yes.
YOU: Will you remember me in one month's time?
CHILD: Yes.
YOU: Will you remember me in one week's time?
CHILD: Yes.
YOU: Will you remember me tomorrow?
CHILD: Yes.
YOU: Will you remember me in another minute?
CHILD: Yes.
YOU: Will you remember me in another second?
CHILD: Yes.
YOU: Knock, knock.
CHILD: Who's there?
YOU: See, you've forgotten me already!

## Just Like Me

YOU: I'm going to tell you a story, but I want you to help me. Each time I stop, I want you to say 'just like me'. OK?
CHILD: OK.
YOU: Once upon a time I went for a walk.
CHILD: Just like me.
YOU: I walked through the village and sat on the green.
CHILD: Just like me.
YOU: Then I went and bought an ice-cream.
CHILD: Just like me.
YOU: Then I went for a stroll in the woods.
CHILD: Just like me.
YOU: I looked up into a very tall tree.
CHILD: Just like me.
YOU: And I saw a monkey in it.
CHILD: Just like me.
YOU: Yes, just like you!

Why did the monkey leave the circus?
It was tired of working for peanuts.

# AUTOMATIC BANK

Bernie Bigspender has two bank accounts which he operates
from various automatic machines outside different branches.
Each account has its own secret, four-digit number which can be
tapped in to give Bernie access to them. The number of one
account is four times that of the other, and is also the other in
reverse. What are the two numbers?

**Answer**
8712 and 2178.

# NOVEL-TY

This drawing represents the title of a famous novel. Do you
recognize it?

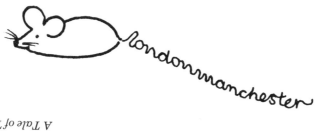

**Answer**
A Tale of Two Cities.

# MONEY GRABBING

Try this trick on a money-grabbing friend. Put a £1 coin on the
floor, near to the wall. Then get your friend to stand with his
back to the wall, and with both head and heels touching it. Then
say that if he can bend down and pick up the coin, without
moving his feet forwards or raising his heels from the floor, he
can keep it. But you won't lose your money – the trick is
impossible.

# TANGRAM TEASERS

These shapes make up the ancient Chinese puzzle called a tangram. They can be used to make a number of other shapes, some of which are illustrated here. How many can you make if you trace the basic puzzle shape off the page and cut it into its component parts?

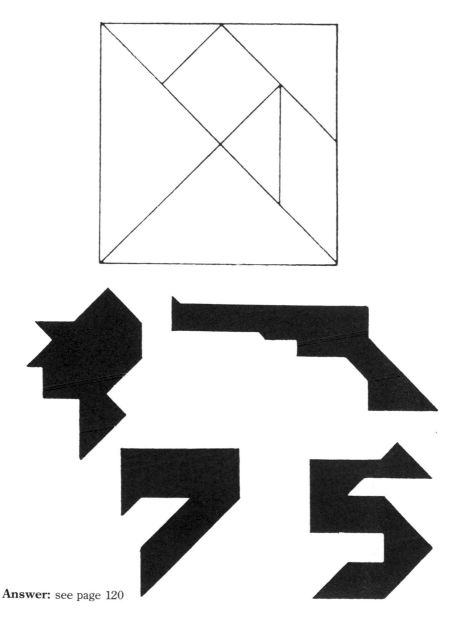

**Answer:** see page 120

# PUSH ME, PULL YOU

This is a test of strength which is best demonstrated by two people of unequal size and strength. They also need a stout stick, such as a walking stick or broomstick.

The weaker friend should hold the stick out horizontally in front of him, with his hands about a foot apart in the centre of the stick. The stronger friend should put his hands on the outside of the other person's, and the idea is that the stronger person tries to push the weaker person over. He must give a steady push, not make any sudden grabs or try pulling instead. But if the weaker person knows the secret – which is to push slightly upwards, rather than simply back towards the other person – they will be immovable.

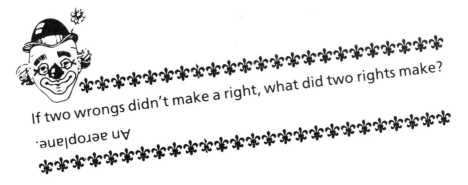

If two wrongs didn't make a right, what did two rights make?

An aeroplane.

# SPELLING BEE

How good is your spelling? Can you spot the words in this list that are spelt incorrectly, and put them right?

accomplishment          nonogenarian
colossal                pneumonia
fuschia                 priviledge
glueing                 reciept
hawser                  spontonaeity
juditious               wildebeest

**Answer**

Fuchsia, gluing, judicious, nonagenarian, privilege, receipt, spontaneity.

# KISSING THE BOOK

Here's a challenge for you. Can you kiss a book inside and outside without opening it?

You should be able to. Because all you need to do is to pick up the book in the house and kiss its cover, then take it outside and kiss its cover again!


# UNQUENCHABLE FLAME

Do you believe there can be such a thing as a candle flame that cannot be blown out? You can prove it if you have a funnel to hand.

Put the lighted candle on the table in front of you. Then, centring the funnel on it, blow as hard as you can. Not only will the candle not go out, but the flame will 'lean' towards the funnel, as if you were sucking instead of blowing.

If you have two paperclips, and a £5 note, or a piece of paper the same size, you can make the clips jump into the air and link themselves together. Here's how you do it.

Fold the note or paper into an 'S' shape, and clip the first loop of the 'S' to its centre with the first paperclip, making sure that it is the shorter loop of the clip that goes over the two thicknesses. Then do the same from the other side of the note, clipping the other loop to the centre with the shorter loop of the paperclip. Then take hold of the two ends of the note, one side with each hand, and give a sharp tug to pull it out straight again. The paperclips will leap into the air and fasten themselves together.

# OIL CAN

By using seven matches, can you turn oil into ink?

**Answer**

## AMAZING EGG

You may need a little practice to succeed with this trick, but it is possible, and extremely impressive. It requires one hard-boiled egg and two wine glasses.

Stand the egg in the first wine glass with about a third of it sticking out of the top. Take a deep breath, and blow hard – and, once you get the distance right, the egg will jump from the first glass into the second. It is quite eggstraordinary!

# SEEING RED

This little phenomenon is very strange, but it usually works. Just try answering the following questions as quickly as possible, without stopping to think for too long.

What's two plus two?
What's four plus two?
What's six plus two?
What's eight plus two?
What's four plus four?
What's four plus six?
What's six plus eight?
What's eight plus eight?
What's ten plus eight?
What's ten plus ten?
What's the first vegetable that comes into your head?

Now, the answer, believe it or not, should be 'carrots'. Unless, of course, you say 'tomatoes', but they, strictly speaking, are not vegetables but fruits. It is very strange, but answering a succession of addition sums is said to produce a sensation of orange or red in your mind, and carrots are one of the few vegetables of this colour.

What can everyone draw, regardless of how good an artist they are?

Their breath.

# WITH A PINCH OF SALT

Now, a paper tissue is a pretty flimsy thing, isn't it? You wouldn't consider that it had much strength. Here's an experiment to prove you wrong. To do it you need a cardboard tube (the inside of a toilet roll or kitchen roll will do), a rubber band, a paper tissue, a thick stick, such as the end of a broom handle, and some salt.

Stretch the tissue over the end of the cardboard tube and hold it in place with the rubber band. You could push the stick through its end easily, couldn't you?

Now pour about two and a half inches of salt into the end of the tube, to be held in place by the tissue. Then push hard with the stick down the tube, trying to break the tissue.

Surprisingly, you will not be able to do so. This is because the grains of salt dissipate your efforts into different directions, so by the time the force meets the tissue itself it has become considerably weaker.

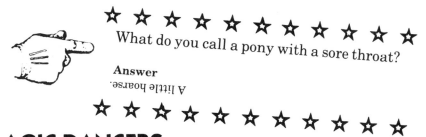

☆ ☆ ☆ ☆ ☆ ☆ ☆ ☆ ☆ ☆ ☆
What do you call a pony with a sore throat?

**Answer**
A little hoarse.

☆ ☆ ☆ ☆ ☆ ☆ ☆ ☆ ☆ ☆ ☆

# MAGIC DANCERS

This little party trick will delight everyone who is young at heart. To do it, you need a sheet of glass, roughly foolscap size, two thick books, a number of little figures cut out of paper, preferably of different colours, and a silk scarf or handkerchief. Failing this, a woollen cloth would do.

Place the glass between the pages of the two books to form a sort of bridge, with the glass about two inches above the table. Cut out a number of the little figures, as if they are leaping or dancing. They should be between half an inch and an inch in height. Lay them on the table beneath the glass sheet.

Warm the scarf, roll it into a ball, and rub the top of the glass vigorously with it. The figures will rise to their feet and dance about, leaping up towards the glass and falling back again. The dancing will continue for a while even after you have stopped rubbing the glass, and after it has eventually stopped, touching the glass with your hand will start it up again.

## GRASPING WITH STRAW

Can you lift a coin off a table by sucking at it through a straw? If
you try, you may think this is an impossible trick, but it can be
done, if you know the secret. And this is simply to wet the end of
the straw. The coin will then adhere to it without any problem,
and as long as you keep breathing in, you will be able to lift it
up. If you want to play a trick on someone, show them how to do
it without revealing that the end of the straw is wet, then
surreptitiously dry it, and the coin, before you let them have a
go. They will be mystified as to how it is done!

## STRONG STRAW

Can you lift an empty bottle with an ordinary paper straw? It
can be done.

When you've finished trying to wrap the straw round the
bottle's neck and tie a knot in it (which is unlikely to work), you
may like to try the easy way. Bend the straw and slide the bent
end inside the neck of the bottle. Then try lifting the bottle with
the straw. Because of the bend, the straw will stick inside the
bottle, and you should be able to lift it quite easily. It is
important, however, to make sure the straw is quite dry, for if it
gets wet it will not work.

# WHISTLE STOP

Try eating a slice of lemon and then giving a little whistle. Can you do it?

How do you hire a table?

Put a brick under each leg.

# DRAUGHTY!

Challenge someone to remove the bottom draught from a stack of six or eight without knocking over all the others, and without touching any of the others. The way to do it is to hit the bottom draught sharply on its side with a ruler or a paper knife. It should move cleanly out of its place, allowing the pile to fall back down again without falling over. The principle is the same as that of the trick in which a tablecloth, laden with crockery, is whipped off a table. If you do it quickly enough, it will work. But it is easier, and cheaper, to start with the draughts!

# LIFT MAN

If you have a young friend who is smaller and weaker than you are, or even a big friend who is obviously much stronger, then try this teaser.

Get the smaller person to stand with his arms up towards his chest and his elbows pointing vertically downwards. The larger person will be able to lift them by the elbows easily. Now, if he moves his elbows forward slightly, so they no longer point vertically downwards, the larger person will have the greatest difficulty in lifting him. Try it and see.

# PIN PUZZLE

Make two tiny holes, about a millimetre apart, with a pin in a sheet of paper. Then hold the pin on the far side of the paper, close one eye, and look at the pin with the other eye. You will see two pins!

Who had a parrot that shouted, 'Pieces of four! Pieces of four!'?

**Answer**
Short John Silver.

# MIND READING

You can do a simple mind-reading trick with a small audience, a few pieces of blank card, a blindfold and some hard and some soft pencils.

Ask each person in the audience to write a boy's or a girl's name on their card, handing each of them a card and a pencil as you do so. Then get someone to blindfold you, ask them to mix up the cards well and offer them back to you. Pick them up one at a time, and by projecting your thoughts on to them, tell your audience which contains the name of a boy and which contains the name of a girl!

The secret is to hand a hard pencil to those people you ask to write a boy's names and a soft pencil to those writing the girls' names. Then, by just running your fingers over the cards, you will be able to detect which is which, for a hard pencil leaves an indentation on the card's surface, whereas a soft pencil does not.

# MAKING MONEY

This trick should appeal to everyone! To do it you need ten coins, some Blu-tack, and a table.

Start by laying out six coins on the table, and inviting the audience to count them as you do so. 'One, two, three, four, five, six.'

You then say, 'Is that right? I'll just count them again,' and sweep them off the table into the palm of your hand as you do so.

Count them out again, 'One, two, three, four, five, six, seven. Seven?' Sweep them off the table to count them again, and lay them out again in front of the audience: 'One, two, three, four, five, six, seven, eight.'

You continue in this way until you have counted out the ten coins, and satisfied yourself, and the audience, that that is the correct number. They, of course, will not know how you do it. The answer is to have the table prepared beforehand with four coins stuck to its under side with Blu-tack, and each time you sweep the coins into the palm of your hand you dislodge one of the hidden coins, so there is always one more than was previously counted.

# HAT TRICK

Have you always wanted to know how magicians produce an endless stream of amazing objects from a top hat? Well, here's one way of doing it. You will need a top hat (or some other kind of hat), a headsquare and several coloured handkerchiefs, a number of small objects – perhaps an egg, a small toy, a bottle of perfume, a tangerine, etc., and a table with a ledge or pile of books on it, behind which things can be concealed.

First, the audience examines the hat to make sure there is nothing inside it. You can make a big show of rolling up your sleeves to show there is nothing hidden there, either. Then pick up the hat, wave your arms over it, say the magic words, and start to produce the silks, the egg, the tangerine, and so on, from inside it.

The trick is to have all the objects concealed in a bundle in the headsquare or large silk beforehand, and to hide the bundle behind the ledge or pile of books on the table. Then, after putting the hat down on the table to show there is nothing up your sleeves, you sweep up the bundle into the hat, making sure the audience cannot see what you are doing. You can then produce each item one at a time and leave behind a very puzzled audience indeed!

# ER, WHAT?

Look at the letters below. Take three other letters, and add them to the front and to the back of the letters below, in the same order each time, to form a perfectly ordinary English word. What is it?

E R G R O

**Answer**

Underground.

# NEIGH!

If a stupid donkey is a CRASS ASS, what might a pantomime horse be?

**Answer**

A phoney pony.

# LETTER, PLEASE

What is the next letter in the series?

G S O G Q, L L O N Q, G S

**Answer**

T. They are the initial letters of the first three lines of the National Anthem.

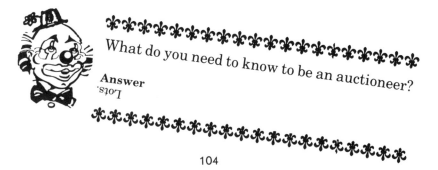

What do you need to know to be an auctioneer?

**Answer**

Lots.

# DAY BY DAZE

When the day before yesterday was called the day after
tomorrow, the day that was then called yesterday was as far
away from the day we now call tomorrow as yesterday is from
the day on which we shall now be able to speak of last Monday as
'a week ago yesterday'. What day is it?

**Answer**

Thursday.

# COMMON DENOMINATOR

What do these six words have in common?

## CALMNESS, CANOPY, DEFT, FIRST, SIGHING, STUN

**Answer**

Each contains three letters of the alphabet in their correct order:
LMN, NOP, DEF, RST, GHI, STU.

# TOEING THE LINE

Which of these two lines is the longer?

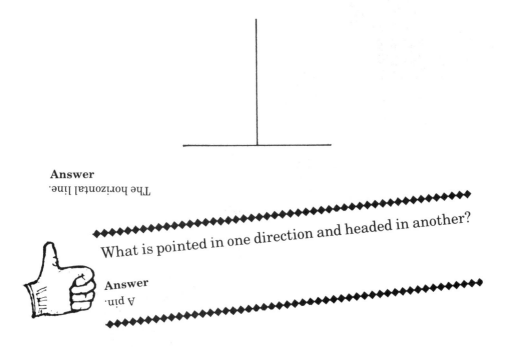

**Answer**
The horizontal line.

What is pointed in one direction and headed in another?

**Answer**
A pin.

# IN THE TUBE

Here's a way to make a scarf appear from an empty paper tube – and amaze your onlookers at the same time. All you need are two sheets of paper or thin cardboard, two paperclips and a thin scarf or handkerchief.

Roll one sheet of paper into a tube and secure it at both ends with a paperclip. Then roll the other sheet into a tube of slightly smaller diameter, with one end rolled a little tighter than the other. Put the smaller tube inside the first tube, holding it in place with the paperclips, too. Slide the scarf between the two tubes, making sure it is smooth and has no creases to give away its presence.

Anyone looking down the tube will be unable to see the scarf, but you will be able to make the scarf appear from it as if by magic.

# EVERLASTING ROPE

This is a simple, amusing and effective trick. All you need to perform it is a thin piece of rope or cord, between six and ten feet in length, and a jacket.

The idea is that you are seen holding about a foot of rope in your left hand. Explain to your audience that you think it's a pity that the rope isn't longer, because then you could use it as a washing line, a dog lead, a skipping rope, or whatever. You then get hold of the front end of the rope and pull it gently. The rope stretches to become two feet long, three feet long, four feet long – and so on, depending on how long it was in the first place. The secret, of course, is that it goes up your sleeve and comes back down again – though no one will be able to tell that!

# MATHEMATICAL MIND-READING

Give a friend a pencil and a piece of paper and tell her to write down a number, anything she likes provided the digits do not decrease in value. That is, it could be 1234, but not 4321.

Then tell her to multiply the number by ten. (You, of course, should be able to see nothing of this.) And then tell her to subtract the original number from the new number. Then tell her to add nine to the result.

Right. Now tell her to cross out any one digit she likes, with the exception of a nought, and to tell you what the remaining digits are. You can then tell her what the digit was that she crossed out. All you do is to add up the remaining digits that she tells you, and deduct the total from nine. What is left is the digit she crossed out. This is how it works.

1. Think of a number. 4589

2. Multiply by ten. 4589 × 10 = 45890

3. Subtract the original number. 45890 − 4589 = 41301

4. Add nine. 41301 + 9 = 41310

5. Cross out any digit except nought. 41310

6. Add the remaining digits and subtract from nine.
   4 + 1 + 1 = 6
   9 − 6 = 3.

7. Three was the digit crossed out.

What do you call two spiders who have just got married?

**Answer**
Newly webs.

How do you spell 'mousetrap' in three letters?

**Answer**
'C-A-T'.

# PUSHING A GLASS THROUGH A TABLE

All you need to do this really effective trick is a glass, a circle of cardboard the same diameter as the top of the glass, a chair, and a table covered with a cloth.

The trick is to sit down at the table holding the glass, take a sip of water from the glass, put the glass under the tablecloth, and then bring a fist down on the glass and apparently push it through the table, bringing it out, undamaged, with the other hand from underneath the table.

The secret is to lift the tablecloth with one hand, but instead of putting the glass under it to quickly slip the glass between your knees, and hold it there while holding the cardboard disc up under the tablecloth so it appears as if the glass is really there. As you bring down your fist to 'knock the glass through the table', you let go of the cardboard disc, and then bring the glass out from under the table, where it has been all the time.

# *THAT'S IT!*

If you add punctuation to the words below, they will make sense. Can you see how to do it?

That that is is that that is not is not is not that it it is

**Answer**
That that is, is; that that is not, is not; is not that it? It is!

# SHIRTY

If a man bought a shirt and a tie for £21, and the shirt cost £20 more than the tie, how much did each cost?

**Answer**

The shirt cost £20.50 and the tie cost 50p.

# OLD BANGER

If Shady Sid, the secondhand car dealer, sold a Mini Cooper for £700 plus half as much as he paid for it, and his profit on the deal was £210, how much did he pay for the car in the first place?

**Answer**

£980.

# PINT SIZED

If Jim drinks two pints of beer in five minutes, and John drinks two pints of beer in two and a half minutes, how long would they take to drink two pints of beer between them?

**Answer**
One and two-thirds minutes.

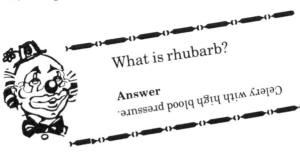

What is rhubarb?

**Answer**
Celery with high blood pressure.

# DOTTY

Can you join these nine dots with four straight lines without taking your pencil off the paper or going over the same line twice?

**Answer:** see page 120

Which Red Indian tribe had the greatest number of lawyers?

**Answer**
The Sioux.

# NUMBER COLUMNS

Write the numbers from 1 to 9 on separate pieces of paper and arrange them like this:

| 2 | 1 |
|---|---|
| 6 | 3 |
| 7 | 4 |
| 9 | 5 |
|   | 8 |

The first column adds up to 24; the second to 21. By moving just one piece of paper, make the totals of the two columns the same.

**Answer**

Turn the 9 in the first column upside down so it becomes a 6.

# THE SILVER EGG

Hold an egg over a candle flame so that it becomes blackened with the soot. Then immerse it in water.

Amazingly the egg appears to have a kind of silvery glow about it, though if you remove it from the water it appears as black as it did before you immersed it.

# A FRUIT THAT PEELS ITSELF

An interesting experiment can be set up using an empty bottle and a banana, in which the fruit can be made to peel itself.

First of all the bottle should be prepared with a substance that will burn – either a few drops of methylated spirit, or a few pieces of paper. Then the banana should have its top cut with a knife, and the four sides peeled back just a little way, to start it off.

A lighted match is dropped into the bottle to ignite the spirit or paper, and just as the flames are dying down, the prepared end of the banana is stuck into the neck of the bottle. Amazingly, the banana will be sucked down into the bottle, peeling off its skin as it goes. Obviously the neck of the bottle has to be wide enough for this to happen or the trick will not work.

# NEXT NUMBER

What's the next number in this series?

31, 28, 31, 30, 31?

**Answer**

30. They are the number of days in the months, starting with January.

# HARRY HAWKINS

If Harry Hawkins is forty, and his daughter Hettie is thirteen, how many years ago was Harry four times as old as Hettie?

**Answer**

Four years ago.

# TOO MUCH

How can you write five twos in a row to make them total 28?

**Answer**

$2 + 2 + 2 + 22 = 28$

# LEAP YEAR

If, on the evening of 28 February in a leap year, you go to bed at 7 p.m., having set your alarm to wake you at 8 a.m., how many hours' sleep will you have?

**Answer**

One! Unless you have a twenty-four hour clock.

# ANGULAR

If you turn these twelve triangles into six squares, what do you get?

**Answer**

THE END.

# ANSWERS

Page 11

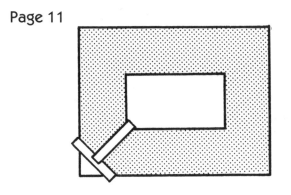

Page 16

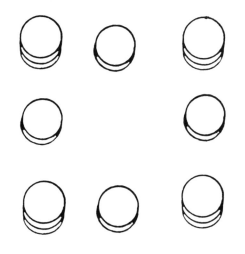

Page 25

Page 34

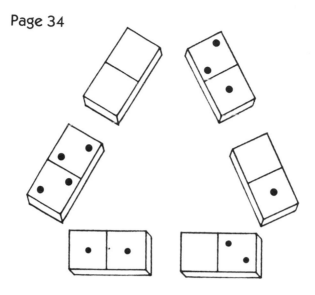

Page 35

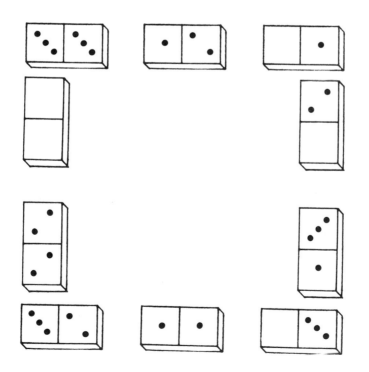

Page 48

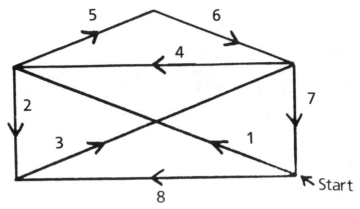

Page 50

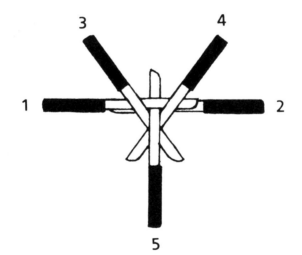

## Page 51  This is how it is done.

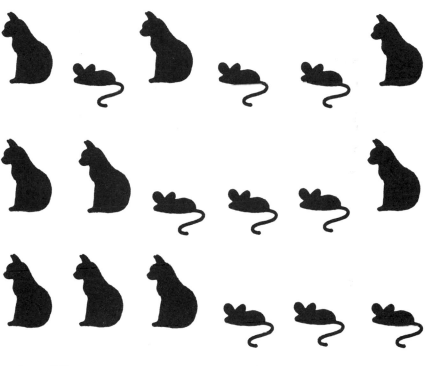

## Page 57

## Page 64

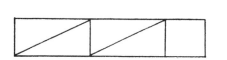

119

**Page 78**

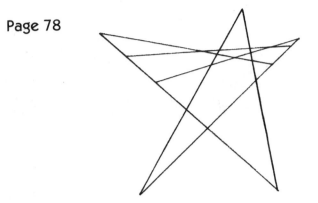

**Page 91**

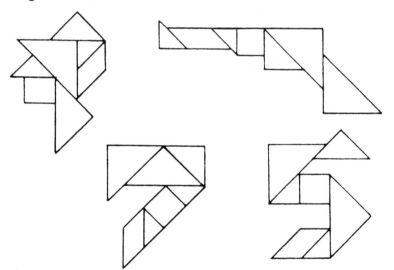

**Page 111**

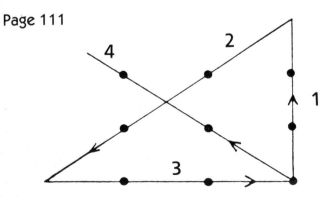